TREASURE ISLAND

A GRAPHIC CLASSIC BY
ADAM GRANT

BASED ON THE NOVEL BY
ROBERT LOUIS STEVENSON

SCHOLASTIC INC.
New York Toronto London Auckland Sydney
Mexico City New Delhi Hong Kong

PENCILLER
MICHAEL LILLY

INKER
SCOTT GOODELL

COLORIST
J. BROWN AND TECH FX

LETTERER
FRED VAN LENTE

COVER ARTIST
MICHAEL LILLY

COVER COLORS
J. BROWN AND TECH FX

Copyright © 1999 by Scholastic Inc.
All rights reserved. Published by Scholastic Inc.
Printed in the U.S.A.

ISBN 0-439-05692-6

SCHOLASTIC, READ 180, and associated logos and designs are
trademarks and/or registered trademarks of Scholastic Inc.
LEXILE is a trademark of MetaMetrics, Inc.

8 9 10   23   06 05 04

TREASURE ISLAND

ROBERT LOUIS STEVENSON WANTED TO BECOME A WRITER. HE ALSO WANTED ADVENTURE. IN 1872, WHEN HE WAS 22, HE STARTED TRAVELING THE WORLD.

HE EXPLORED EUROPE. THEN HE WENT TO SAN FRANCISCO. THERE, HE MET AND MARRIED A WOMAN NAMED FANNY OSBOURNE, WHO HAD A SON, LLOYD.

STEVENSON WROTE HIS FIRST NOVEL, TREASURE ISLAND, TO ENTERTAIN HIS NEW STEPSON LLOYD. IT WAS AN EXCITING TALE ABOUT PIRATES, A MYSTERIOUS MAP, AND BURIED TREASURE.

IN 1888, STEVENSON AND HIS FAMILY MOVED TO THE ISLAND OF SAMOA. HE WAS VERY SICK, AND HE HOPED HE'D FEEL BETTER IN A WARM CLIMATE.

STEVENSON ONLY LIVED SIX MORE YEARS. BUT HE MANAGED TO WRITE MANY GREAT TALES—AND TRAVEL THE WORLD.

BONES CAUSED LOTS OF TROUBLE FOR MY MOTHER AND ME. HE SPENT MANY NIGHTS DRINKING AND SINGING HIS STRANGE SEA SONGS.
Fifteen men on a dead man's chest! Yo ho ho and a bottle of rum!
BILLY BONES ALSO TOLD STRANGE STORIES FROM HIS DAYS SAILING WITH A FAMOUS PIRATE CALLED CAPTAIN FLINT.
... We had already fed most of his crew to the sharks. And I said to him, "You're next, Admiral. If you can't walk the plank yourself, I'll be glad to help you!"
ONE DAY, BONES OFFERED ME A FEW PENNIES IF I WOULD DO A LITTLE JOB FOR HIM.
Keep your eye open for a seafaring man with one leg, Jim. My life depends on it.

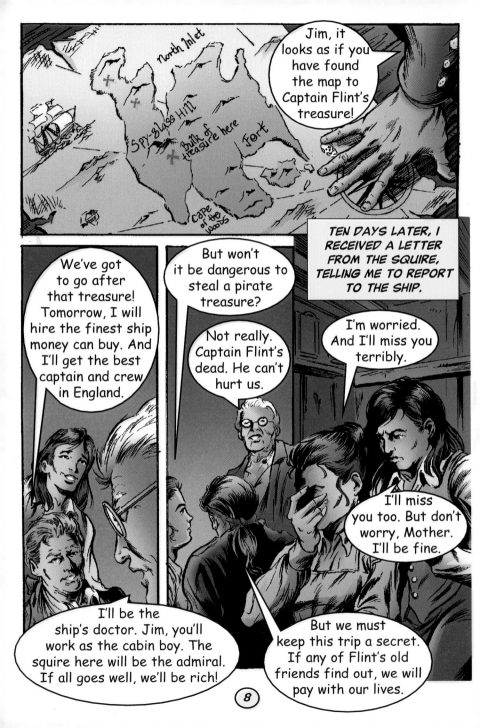

THAT AFTERNOON, THE BATTLE BEGAN. THE PIRATES QUICKLY HAMMERED THEIR WAY INTO THE FORT.

SOMEHOW, WE KEPT OUR HEADS. SOON, A FEW OF THE PIRATES HAD FALLEN. WITHIN MINUTES, THE REST OF THEM WERE HEADED BACK TO THE TREES. I WAS SURE THE FORT AND THE MAP WERE STILL OURS!

THEN I THOUGHT OF SOMETHING. THE PIRATES WERE ALL FIGHTING US. SO WHO WAS GUARDING THE SHIP? MAYBE I COULD STEAL IT BACK FOR US. I KNEW MY FRIENDS WOULDN'T LIKE THIS PLAN. SO AS SOON AS IT WAS DARK, I SNEAKED AWAY.

I WENT TO THE SPOT WHERE BEN GUNN HAD TOLD ME HE HAD A BOAT. SURE ENOUGH, IT WAS THERE.

I FOUND THE *HISPANIOLA* ANCHORED IN THE BAY. IT LOOKED LIKE THERE WASN'T A SOUL ON BOARD. I CLIMBED UP THE ANCHOR ROPE.

THE DECK WAS COVERED WITH BODIES. THE PIRATES SILVER HAD LEFT TO GUARD THE SHIP HAD KILLED EACH OTHER! BUT THEN I SAW ONE OF THE BODIES MOVE....

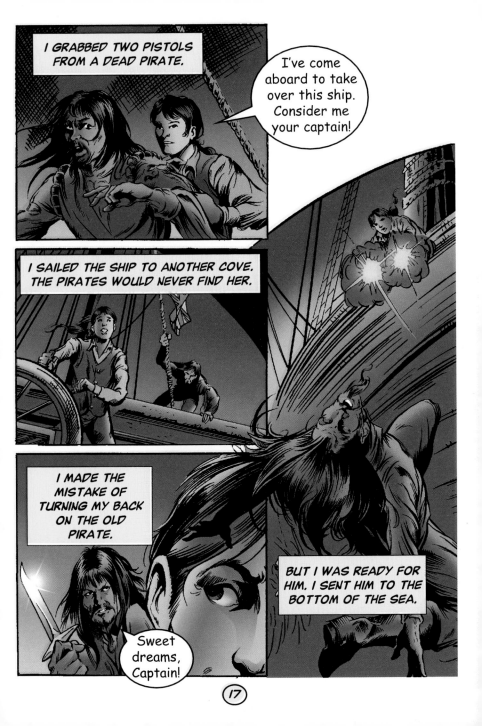

I SWAM BACK TO SHORE AND HEADED FOR THE FORT. IT WAS PITCH BLACK IN THERE. I GUESSED THAT MY FRIENDS WERE ALREADY FAST ASLEEP.

I WAS CRAWLING TO MY BUNK WHEN MY FOOT HIT SOMETHING

SOMEHOW, THE PIRATES HAD TAKEN THE FORT. I WAS IN ENEMY CAMP.

Pieces of eight! Pieces of eight! BRAAWK!

Shiver me timbers, here's Jim Hawkins! I always wanted you to join us pirates, and now you've got to!

We ran your friends out of here. They probably think you're dead. So you're either our mate, or our hostage.

SILVER TOLD ME HOW THAT DAY, DR. LIVESEY HAD COME TO THE PIRATE CAMP TO BARGAIN.

The doctor realized that his men couldn't beat us. He gave us the fort in exchange for food and safe passage to the other side of the island.

There's a thing or two I must tell you, Silver.

So you're stuck with us. Why not join us?

You're in a bad situation. Your ship is lost. Your treasure is lost. And you're stuck on this island. And you know who did it? Me! I hid behind the apple barrel and heard your evil scheme. I told it to the captain and the squire. I killed your last man on the *Hispaniola.* And I hid the ship where you'll never find her!

19

SUDDENLY, A PIRATE JUMPED OUT AT ME.
And it was *you* who stole the map from Billy Bones in the first place! Well, lad, here's my sword!
I WAS RELIEVED—AND VERY SURPRISED—WHEN SILVER CAME TO MY RESCUE.
I'll thank you to shut up till you're spoken to!
And that goes for all of you. I'm captain here, and I like the boy. He's more of a man than any *two* of you rats!
Anyway, I've got a surprise for you whining old ladies. It's the treasure map. I got it from the good doctor. So you see, lads, you'll be rich men after all!
Barbecue forever! Hurrah for Captain Barbecue!

JUST THEN, THREE SHOTS RANG OUT. TWO OF THE PIRATES DROPPED DEAD, AND THE OTHER THREE RAN OFF.

MY FRIENDS HAD WAITED IN THE WOODS AND ATTACKED THE PIRATES. I WAS NEVER SO GLAD TO SEE ANYONE IN MY LIFE.

IT SEEMS THAT OVER THE PAST FEW YEARS, BEN GUNN HAD DUG UP MOST OF FLINT'S TREASURE AND HID IT AWAY IN HIS CAVE.

It's not all of it, but it's enough, I reckon.

I know, sir. I ran off without telling anyone. But I did get the ship back from the pirates and hid her.

That's why I traded away the map, Jim. Gunn told us it was worthless. I hated to leave you with those criminals, but I had to look after the others.

22

AFTER A FEW DAYS, WE LANDED IN SOUTH AMERICA AND WENT ASHORE.

WHEN WE RETURNED TO THE SHIP, WE HAD A SHOCK. OUR WATCHMAN, BEN GUNN, HAD BEEN KNOCKED OUT. YOU-KNOW-WHO WAS GONE.

SILVER HAD ESCAPED. AND HE HAD STOLEN A SACK OF OUR HARD-WON COINS.

We're lucky to be rid of him. And we're lucky it didn't cost us more.

I HAVE HEARD NO MORE OF LONG JOHN SILVER. BUT I GUESS HE'S LIVING SOMEWHERE COMFORTABLY WITH HIS STOLEN TREASURE.

THE REST OF FLINT'S SILVER COINS STILL LIE, I IMAGINE, WHERE THE OLD PIRATE LEFT THEM. AND THEY CAN STAY THERE, FOR ALL I CARE.

WILD HORSES COULD NOT DRAG ME BACK TO THAT ISLAND. THE WORST DREAMS THAT I HAVE EVER HAD ARE WHEN I HEAR THE SURF BOOMING ON THE COAST OR SIT UP IN BED WITH THE SHARP VOICE OF SILVER'S BIRD, FLINT, RINGING IN MY EARS ...